Double Your Fun

Written by Jordan Brown
Illustrated by Donna Reynolds

This is a PAWS book.
When you see Jake's paw, STOP!
Answer the question.

http://www.sf.aw.com

ISBN: 0-201-31777-X

Printed in the United States of America.

2 3 4 5 6 7 8 9 10-BX-01 00 99 98 97

C.J. flew to the tree house one sunny day.

"Annie, I have great news," C.J. said.
"The Silly Shop is having a sale!"

"I love that store!" Annie said.

"Let's go!" C.J. yelled.

"Wait!" Annie said. She turned over her bank.

Annie frowned. "I don't have very much money."

"No problem," C.J. said. "It's a 2-for-1 sale. If you buy 1 toy, you get another toy for free!"

"Great!" Annie said. "Let's go!"

If you buy one, you get another one free!

Annie looked in the silly mirror
outside the store. It made her
look tall and thin.

"Look, there are 2 of me in the
mirror!" Annie said. "We both
look so skinny!"

A man came out of the
store.

"Welcome to my store.
I'm Mr. Clucky," he said
"Come inside and do
some double shopping!"

Silly Shop
2 for 1 Sale!
Mr. Clucky

Mr. Clucky gave Annie a basket.

"Here is a special basket for double shopping!" he said. "First, you put a toy on the BUY side. Then, you can put the same toy on the FREE side."

Annie started with 4 cans of the Smelly Sock Powder.

She put 4 cans in the BUY side of the basket. Then she put 4 more cans in the FREE side.

How many cans of powder does Annie have in all?

When you double four, you get four more!
Smelly Sock Powder
Buy
Free
Silly Shop

"I get 8 cans of powder!" Annie said. "What should we get next?"

"How about a Bubble Fish?" Mr. Clucky said.

"Why are they called Bubble Fish?" Annie asked.

Mr. Clucky turned the crank on the side of the fish. Bubbles floated out!

"Wow!" Annie yelled. "I can buy 5 Bubble Fish."

How many Bubble Fish will Annie get if she buys 5?

Mr
BubbleFish

"If I buy 5 Bubble Fish, I get 5 free. That's 10," Annie said.

C.J. grabbed a basket. "I want a messy toy," she said.

"I know just the thing!" Mr. Clucky said. "Goopy Goop!"

C.J. put 6 balls of Goopy Goop on each side of her basket.

How many balls of Goopy Goop does C.J. have in all?

Goopy
GOOP
Goopy
GOO
Mr. Clucky
Buy
Free
Yuck! This goop sure is messy.

"That's 12 balls of Goopy Goop!" C.J. said.

"I want to buy Funny Forks for a party at school," Annie said.

"How many children are in your class?" Mr. Clucky asked.

"14," Annie answered.

"So we need to buy only 7 forks," C.J. said.

7 doubled is
fork-teen.
I mean, 14.
Free
OP

"Look!" C.J. shouted. "Sticky Critters!"

Mr. Clucky said, "They are my best seller! You get 8 in a pack."

C.J. stuck a rubber bug right on Annie's nose.

"I can buy 1 pack! That's only 8 Sticky Critters."

"Remember, C.J.," Mr. Clucky said, "today everything you buy gets doubled!

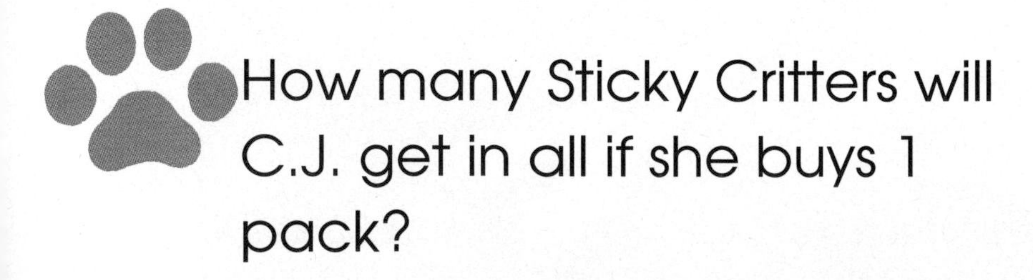

How many Sticky Critters will C.J. get in all if she buys 1 pack?

Sticky Critters
Sticky Critters
This is really starting to bug me!

"I get 16 Sticky Critters in all!" C.J. said. "That is double the fun!"

Jake ran into the store. He saw his friends covered with bugs.

"I will save you!" Jake cried.

Annie laughed. "It's a 2-for-1 sale, Jake," she said. "Everything you buy gets doubled today. Even rubber bugs."

"I'm glad you are all right," Jake said. "I thought my nose smelled double trouble!"

Silly Shop
2 for 1 Sale!

"Did you say nose?" Mr. Clucky asked. "I have a great new toy for you! It's the Noisy Nose Horn."

Mr. Clucky gave one to Jake and said, "Okay, blow your nose!"

Everyone laughed.

Jake said, "I will buy 9 of these."

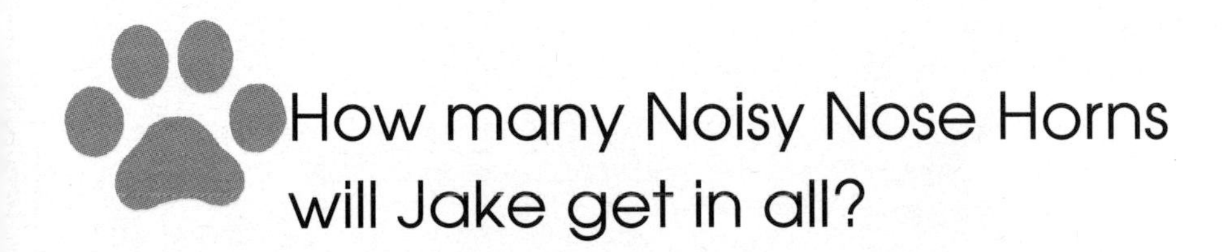

How many Noisy Nose Horns will Jake get in all?

Noisy Nose Horns
Buy
Free

"9 doubled is 18," Jake said. "I have 18 nose horns in all!"

Mr. Clucky packed up all their toys.

"This was the best sale ever, Mr. Clucky," Annie said. "I wish there was some way we could thank you."

C.J. grabbed her guitar. "I know a way! I made up a song just for your sale."

oopy
oop

C.J. sang her song.

"4 cans turn to 8 — when you double.
5 fish turn to 10 — when you double.
6 balls turn to 12 — when you double.
7 forks turn to 14 — when you double.
8 bugs turn to 16 — when you double.
9 horns turn to 18 — when you double.
Double your fun at the Silly Shop!
Double your fun at the Silly Shop!"